GEMMA O'NEILL

MONTY'S
MAGNIFICENT
MANE

templar publishing

Meet Monty, King of the Jungle.
Monty's favourite thing is his long,
curly, colourful mane.

No one else has a mane quite like his.

Monty thinks it's **magnificent**.

"Monty, your mane is gorgeous and glowing and the longest in the jungle," say his friends, the meerkats.

Monty likes hearing this very much. So he lets the meerkats play in his lovely orange hair…

But they tug and tickle and it's rather annoying.
To get them off, he rumbles, grumbles

and rolls…

CRASH!

Monty ends up taking a tumble.
Now his mane is matted
and covered in dirt!

The meerkats try and make it better,
but they get carried away and give
Monty a brand new look.

He is **not** amused.

So he shuffles

and shakes off the feathers…

… and stomps off to the waterhole to check his reflection.

"Monty!" says one little meerkat as he leaves.
"Remember to be careful of the…"

But Monty is too busy stomping to hear.

At the waterhole, Monty sees a little creature, with cheeky, twinkly eyes.

"My, what a wonderful mane you have," says the creature to Monty.
"In fact, some might say it's magnificent.
Why don't you come a little closer so I can see it better?"

Monty is very proud.
Fluffing out his mane, he
prances closer to his new friend.

He gets closer…

and closer…

and closer…

until…

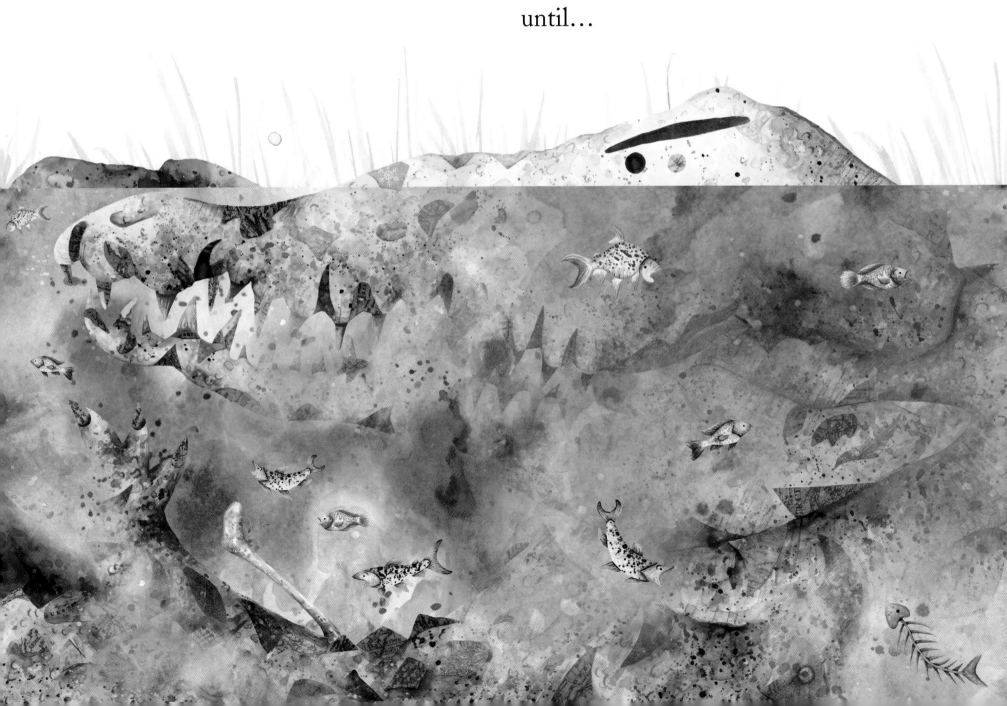

It's a **huge** crocodile!

Monty leaps away, but not before losing
a big bite out of his beautiful mane.
"Come back here!" shouts the crocodile.
"I'm having you for my dinner."

So Monty runs as fast as he can for home.

When he gets there, Monty realises he's made a **terrible** mistake.
The crocodile has followed him all the way.

"Meerkats!" gloats the hungry creature.
"My favourite!"

Now, the meerkats might mess up his mane sometimes,
but they're Monty's friends. He can't let the
crocodile eat them!

But what can he do?

Then Monty remembers something
he can do. Something that's really
rather magnificent.

So he throws back his head…

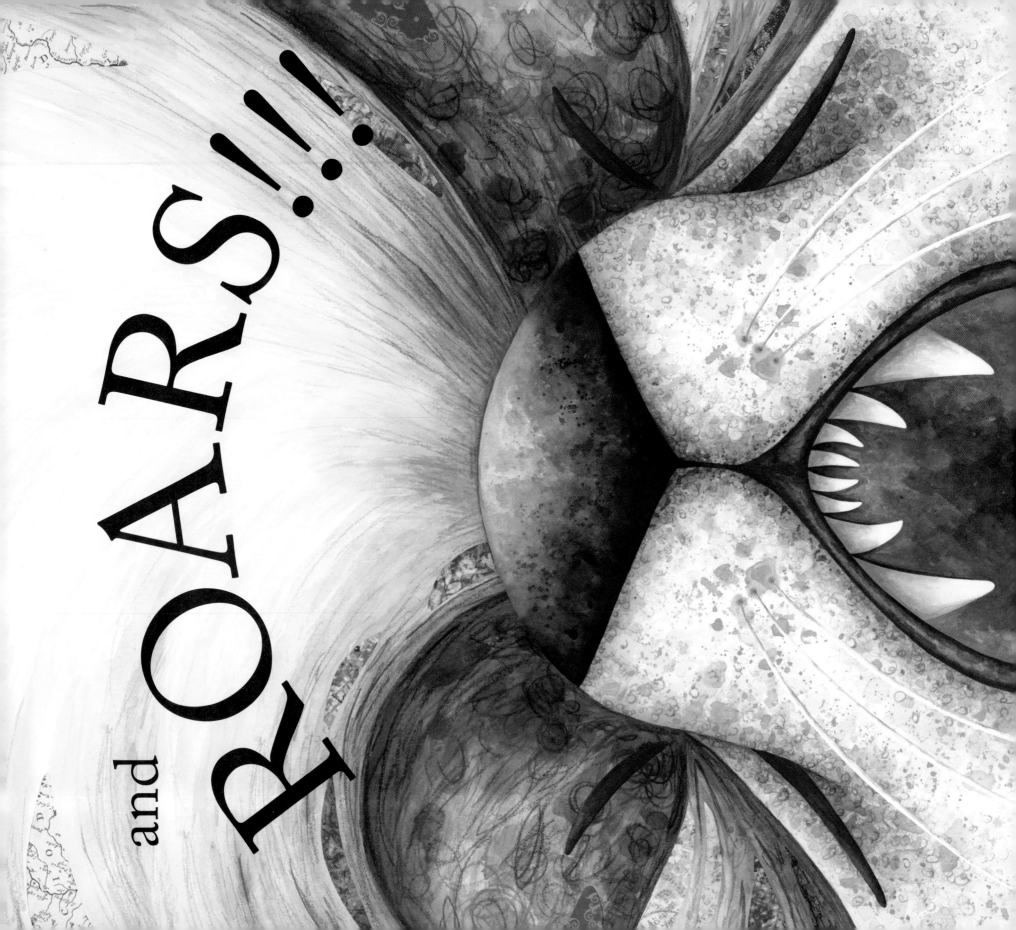

and ROARS!!!

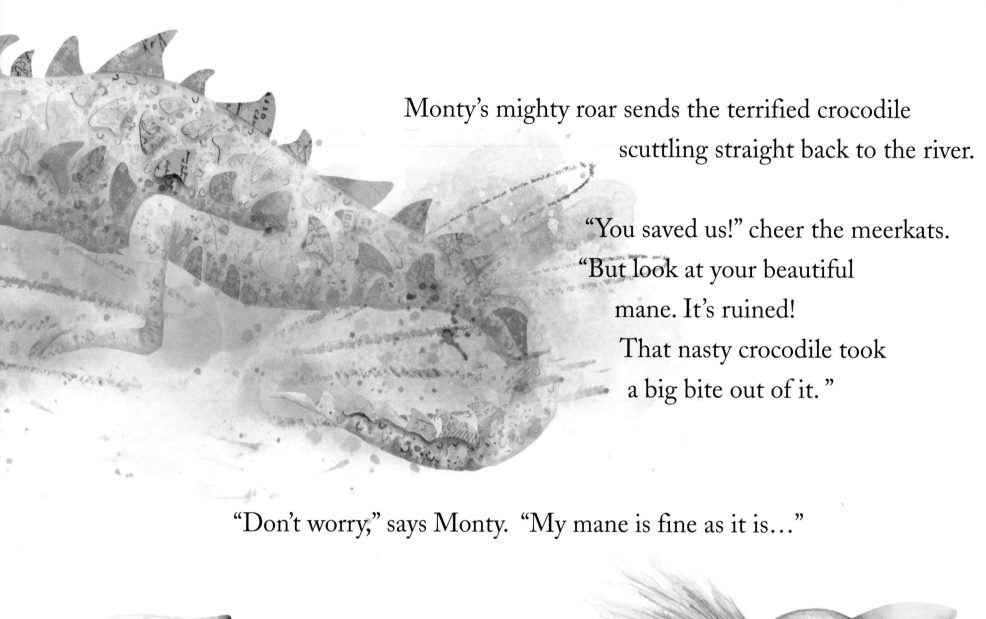

Monty's mighty roar sends the terrified crocodile
scuttling straight back to the river.

"You saved us!" cheer the meerkats.
"But look at your beautiful
mane. It's ruined!
That nasty crocodile took
a big bite out of it."

"Don't worry," says Monty. "My mane is fine as it is…"

"It's the **perfect** place
for my friends to play."